TEXTUAL NOTES

Composition   Munich, Jan–Feb 1775

Source   autograph (formerly in Preussische Staatsbibliothek, Berlin)

Notes

1st movt
bar

57	RH slur may begin on *f"*♯
107	Mozart misplaced the LH treble clef, giving *1* as F♯

3rd movt
bar

35,37	our notation follows Mozart's, perhaps suggesting accent on first note (also 206, 208)
43–4	original (except RH, *50*) has bars slurred singly
49–50	cf. 41–2, 214–15, 220–3
99–100	Mozart originally wrote all notes stacc., then changed to slurs

Abbreviations in Textual Notes

cf. – *confer* [compare]; dsq – demisemiquaver; edn – edition; K – no. in Köchel catalogue of Mozart's works (no. before / is original no., no. after is that in 6th edn, 1964); LH – left hand; movt – movement; q – quaver; RH – right hand; sq – semiquaver; stacc. – staccato

Pitch – *c'* is middle C, *d'* the note above, *b* the note below; *c''* and *c'''* one and two octaves above, *c, C* and *C'* one, two and three octaves below

Numerals – arabic numerals in roman normally denote bar nos.; arabic in italic denote note nos. within the bar, counting left to right, chords downwards, and including all grace notes as notated

Editorial notes

In the printing of the text a distinction has been made between original and editorial markings. Slurs and ties added editorially are indicated by a small perpendicular stroke; editorial staccato marks (whether dots or wedges), dynamic markings and accidentals are indicated by the use of smaller type.

Editorial realizations of ornaments are shown in small notes above the text at the first occurrence of the ornament concerned in each movement. These realizations are based on the leading sources contemporary with Mozart, such as C. P. E. Bach's *Versuch über das wahre Art das Clavier zu spielen* (1753–62), Leopold Mozart's *Versuch einer gründlichen Violinschule* (1756) and Daniel Gottlob Türk's *Clavierschule* (1789). Our suggestions should not be taken as mandatory; any proper realization must take account of the tempo chosen for the movement concerned and the player's capabilities, and in a trill a player should feel free to play more notes, or fewer, as seems right. No ornament that feels awkward to the player, or sounds clumsy, is being satisfactorily realized. A player who wants to vary the realization of ornaments more extensively, however, would be well advised first to consult the writings of contemporary authorities, or failing that a summary of their views in a good modern reference work; he should note that except in very rare circumstances a trill should begin on the upper note in music of this period.

SONATA in G

K283/189h (1774-5)

A.B.1604

Andante

* see Textual Notes

14

A.B.1604

Reproduced and printed by
Halstan & Co. Ltd., Amersham, Bucks., England